ADVANCE

WORK

A PERSONAL

PROTECTION

ASSIGNMENT

7-DAY WORKBOOK

*... and stuff I wish I knew
before I started adulting*

MELANIE LENTZ

Former U.S. Secret Service Special Agent

ISBN: 978-1-7369056-0-9

KDP Publishing
www.kdp.amazon.com

www.melanielentz.com

Cover design and interior art by Melanie Lentz
Author photo by Mac Karr
Oops Detection and formatting by Victory Editing

DEDICATION

To the people who've shown me what it means to empower and live meaningfully

ACKNOWLEDGMENTS

To Mom, Dad, Traci, and Alex. Thank you for always believing in me. I love you all so very much. Thank you for your support even when I was absentee and for staying up till one a.m. to finish all of my projects.

Thank you to the real friends who've stuck around despite my dysfunction and the real friends who make it easy to grant access. Thank you for calling me out when I need it. Britney, Adisa, Kelli K, Rumaisa, Chantelle, Jenna, Jen, etc., you're all keepers.

To my Monday writing crew and our fantastic teacher, Lisa Fugard, I love you all to bits. Lisa F, Lisa W, Melanie R, Lauren, and Rhea. You make me a better writer. I look forward to being pushed to write more profound and more complex in a safe place to "go there." I appreciate you far more than you know.

Jennifer T., Jen S., Kate and Aaliyah, thank you for your thoughtful notes and input during those final drafts.

Thank you to Women Lead Change CEO Tiffany O'Donnell for booking me for my first speaking gig and more. Your willingness to help me grow and share my story authentically is a true example of empowerment.

Laura Harrison, thank you for the opportunities you have provided to me and your kindness to me since we met.

And last but not least, my Mac. Thank you for your straightforward and constructive approach to life. I admire and respect the man you are, and your presence in my life is a blessing I cherish every day. I love you.

INTRODUCTION

Welcome to *Advance Work: A Personal Protection Assignment*. Wherever you are in life, it's never too late to start protecting yourself, inside and out. I hope that the next seven days are enlightening and thought-provoking. Self-protection is not easy, but it's part of self-care.

I wish self-care was merely a pedicure and sleeping in on weekends, but there's more to it. The real self-work can be excruciating and, in my case, life-altering.

My name is Melanie Lentz, and I'm fifty shades of messed up, just like everyone else. My story is a complicated one with low points and fresh starts sprinkled into a few dysfunctional relationships and mistakes. I don't have all of the answers, and I've had to tell myself that repeatedly throughout the process of creating this workbook. Imposter syndrome has been the primary obstacle in this project. I'm afraid I'll miss something important you should know, and maybe someone else is more qualified to write this workbook.

However, at the end of this workbook, I hope my perspective on self-love and protection is helpful as we look at your self-protection this week.

I became a U.S. Secret Service agent when I was twenty-two years old, one of the youngest female agents ever hired to date. I had no military, law enforcement, or life experience going into training. But I was determined to do something meaningful with my life. I got the job and the opportunity to be trained as an expert in physical protection at a young age.

1

The Secret Service is responsible for protecting the president and immediate family members, the vice president and immediate family members, former presidents and spouses, visiting foreign heads of state, and a few others sprinkled in there for good measure.

When I first applied to the Secret Service, I envisioned myself rappelling out of a helicopter to swoop up the president just in the nick of time. I was ready to take on the world and protect the president with my life. I got the black business suit, practiced my tough facial expressions, and purchased the sunglasses. After all, I wanted to look the part of a protector too.

I learned early on that I'd watched too much overdramatized and inaccurate television. In reality, protection is far more than merely showing up in a presidential motorcade and being a human shield as the protectee moves around.

It's the behind-the-scenes work that makes protection assignments safe for everyone. This work is "advance work." If the Secret Service receives notice that the president is planning to attend an event, a team of agents called the "advance team" arrive ahead of the visit to put the security plan together.

The advance team coordinates all of the complicated logistics that come with every assignment. Agents will plan and secure motorcade routes with local law enforcement. Other agents will investigate any threats leading up to the visit. More agents will prepare the most efficient way to secure a venue and control access to ensure the president can move around safely.

There are countless meetings, briefings, diagrams, and staffing to coordinate. However, despite the workload, quality advance work is crucial to a successful assignment.

I'll admit it. I loved advance work! Advance work felt like a problem I could solve. If I had a venue or a site to secure, I had fun figuring out creative ways to put the plan together effectively.

Here's the thing, though. I was good at spotting potential problems in a protection assignment at work. But I neglected the problems in my own life. Neglect caught up with me as neglect tends to do, right?

Eventually, I realized I needed to put my protection expertise to work in my life. It was the hardest thing I've ever done. But it was worth it. I didn't see it then, but I do now.

I gave my life a threat assessment like I would have done as an agent. I realized I had let certain people and situations control my actions and thoughts. I allowed negative influences to compromise my well-being.

In other words, my threat assessment lacked boundaries. I needed to exercise healthier access control, something we'll cover this week at length.

Threat assessment and access control are skills none of us will get right the first time. We'll inevitably make mistakes along the way. I still make mistakes, and I'm the one writing the workbook about it. (Didn't I already mention I'm fifty shades of messed up like everyone else?)

WHAT TO EXPECT
FROM THIS WORKBOOK

Each day we will work and reflect on a different part of self-protection. I'll share my journal entries and stories about how I'm working through the process of self-protection. Each time I ponder it all, I realize that I learn and grow with each mistake. My security "lapses" can be rough, but I've come out of them with more wisdom.

We're going to start by talking about legacy. From there, we'll spend some time discussing the concept of access control, which, as you'll see, is the key factor to healthy self-protection. After looking at our access control, we'll move on to situation reports or status updates. (Yes, you'll learn some Secret Service terminology as we go.)

Then we'll think about how you can help those around you with their self-protection, focusing on being the kind of person who makes others feel empowered and encouraged. And, finally, we'll take what we've learned about ourselves and create actionable goals and decisions for our future.

I want this week to feel like we're having a conversation over coffee. When I meet a friend for coffee or a run, I always say we're "contemplating life" because sometimes just talking it out helps bring clarity to some of the more difficult decisions and situations we're dealing with at the time. That's what I hope you get out of this workbook: some glimpses of clarity and awareness going forward.

I cannot give you the answers. I can't tell you how many times I wished someone would have just told me what to do when faced with a tough decision. Life just doesn't work that way. But we can grow and learn by sharing the tools we've learned along the way.

I'm going to be vulnerable with you as I share how I've learned to protect myself better. I encourage you to do the same with yourself. Allow yourself to feel and let your intuition shine.

But first things first, I want you to remember this for the next week:

You are both the protector and the protectee. A protector knows the person is worth protecting. In other words, *you* are worth protecting, and acknowledging that fact is the first step in your advance work. You can do this! Grab a pen, and let's get started!

REMINDER
You are worth protecting!

and you're amazing!

DAY 1:

WHAT IS YOUR LEGACY?

During my last year as a Secret Service agent, I was assigned to former first lady Nancy Reagan. The Secret Service protects former presidents and their spouses for life. Even though former president Ronald Reagan had passed away, Mrs. Reagan still had Secret Service protection at her home in Los Angeles, CA.

In March 2016, Mrs. Reagan passed away. My supervisor told us that we would protect her until she was laid to rest. That meant someone had to be in the embalming room for her burial preparations. I was in the room for most of that time. Let me tell you, it was a very tough event to watch and one I'll never forget.

At the time, I was going through a divorce. My ex-husband had moved out about two months prior, and I was "alone" for the first time in my adult life. I had recently been diagnosed with depression. I felt like an all-around mess. I began to face some of my more giant life demons, but I had barely scratched the surface. I was still an angry and bitter woman.

I didn't know Mrs. Reagan well. I protected her, but we didn't chat or hang out while I worked. We never had a personal conversation the entire time I was with her! To me, she was just the woman I protected, and being at work was a welcome distraction from my problems in my personal life.

As I look back, Mrs. Reagan's death was a turning point in my life. While I stood at my post during her funeral, I listened to speakers talk about her legacy, mostly her fierce love for her husband and how protective she was throughout their marriage. At first, I was jealous of her seemingly perfect marriage since mine no longer existed. There's an entire book of the love letters Ronald Reagan wrote to Mrs. Reagan over the years. *I Love You, Ronnie: The Letters of Ronald Reagan to Nancy Reagan.* I read them over and over and wanted what she had.

The week after Mrs. Reagan died, I got transfer orders from the Secret Service. My reassignment was to Washington D.C., and I had four months to report to my new assignment. I had some decisions to make, and about ten days before I was supposed to start my new position, I texted my supervisor and told him I was leaving the Secret Service.

I thought I'd lost my mind, but I was actually about to start finding myself.

I know that sounds a little cliché, but it's true. I had been Special Agent Melanie Lentz since I'd finished college. Suddenly, I was just Melanie Lentz, and I had no idea who I was anymore. I didn't like the person I'd become, that's for sure.

I think we all are searching for purpose and identity.

When asked who we want to be, we tend to default to occupational answers.

I want to be an astronaut.

I want to be a dentist.

I want to be an author.

I want to be [insert your dream job].

But legacy is much more than a job. I know it might come across as morbid to think about, but how do you want to be remembered? I'm not talking about after you die. I'm talking about today. How will people remember you if they meet you today?

That was a scary thought to me after Mrs. Reagan died. But a few months later, when I could get past my anger at my circumstances, I realized something: I don't have to know all of the specifics about my future. I don't have to know what my occupation will be or where my life will take me in five, ten, or twenty years.

But I did need to answer this question:

WHAT KIND
OF PERSON
DO YOU WANT
TO BE?

We are going to focus on this question today. Minus logistics, what kind of person do you want to be despite whatever circumstances life throws your way?

Yes, it's a loaded question.

I wrote my answer a few months after I left the Secret Service. I was still depressed and still hurting deeply, but the words I wrote that night are still valid for me today. I'm sharing my journal entry (in all its unedited glory!) for you today, and then you'll spend some time reflecting on how you would answer the same question.

"How do you want to be remembered, Melanie Lentz?

I want people to say I was what love looked like.

I want to be remembered as kind, for kindness stems from love.

I want to be remembered as strong, because a strong lover fights for herself, for her loved ones, and those who can't fight for themselves.

I want to be remembered as lovely because a lovely person transcends the superficial descriptions of sexy, cute, hot, et cetera. A lovely person is beautiful because she loves.

I want to be remembered as modest in the classiest of ways, for a woman who loves herself respects herself enough to learn her true worth, which goes beyond measurements, size, and pressures to overexpose.

I want to be remembered as honest, for honesty itself is a reflection of love in its purest form. Honest love is transparent love, and she's not afraid to show it even if fear and rejection have tainted her past. She just honestly loves anyway.

I want to be remembered as motivated and productive, for a motivated and productive woman doesn't bask in the conveniences of idleness but hustles and produces. She can stand on her own because she loves herself enough to take care of herself.

I want to be remembered as a rejuvenator, for no real woman is a drain on those around her. A rejuvenator loves herself enough to know that building others up is fulfilling in and of itself. Breaking others down to feel full is not love. It's selfish, and selfishness has no place in love. Self-love, yes. Selfishness, no.

I want to be remembered as a fighter, for a woman who fights for what is right is a lover. She won't run at the first sign of trouble. She's committed to her life and those in it. She's not afraid to stand and exchange if it means saving something worth fighting for.

I want to be remembered as humble, never too good for anything. Even if she's a real lady, she's never superior. Never entitled. Never afraid to get her hands dirty and pitch in to help others. She's not afraid to get out of her comfort zone because she loves enough to get the job done.

I want to be remembered because I loved so very hard."

-Melanie Lentz Journal Entry, October 2016

Your Advance Work assignment today is to reflect on what you want your legacy to be. What kind of person do you want to be? Maybe you need to take a break and come back to write later. As I said, my answer came to me in the middle of the night.

Don't force the answer or write something you think others want you to say. Please give it some thought because the rest of the week will build upon the idea of protecting you and the person you want to be.

LEGACY ADVANCE WORK:

WHAT KIND OF PERSON DO YOU WANT TO BE?

_____

_____

_____

_____

_____

_____

_____

_____

_____

_____

_____

_____

_____

REMINDER

You don't have to have all of the logistics figured out to know what kind of legacy you want for your life.

You're doing amazing!

DAY 2:

ACCESS CONTROL OVERVIEW

Access control is the core of protection in the Secret Service. They have someone to protect, and controlling access to that person is crucial to success.

For example, let's say the vice president is scheduled to attend a luncheon for a charity foundation. The advance team is assigned, and they head to the venue. They learn the event is a catered luncheon of twenty-five guests followed by a roundtable Q&A with the foundation's head. This Q&A will be televised on local news channels.

There will be people close to the protectee. There will be the attendees, catering staff, television crews, a Q&A moderator, tech and sound team, probably someone assigned to hair and makeup for the televised portion, and possibly others.

When the Secret Service looks at an event like this, they'll typically place people into one of four categories. People will either have access granted, denied, limited, or revoked.

First things first, everyone in the luncheon room will be "name-checked" (i.e., background checked by the agency) and screened before entry via magnetometers (like the screening everyone goes through at the airport).

Anyone whose name check comes back clear can attend. Before entry, they'll be screened, and access will be granted if there are no issues.

Let's say a background check on a catering staff member reveals something sketchy. This person's access would be denied, and there'd be a semi-awkward conversation with catering management about providing a replacement.

But what about people who need access to the event but not necessarily a seat at the table? For instance, the person assigned to hair and makeup and the sound crew will probably need to do touchups and set up a lapel microphone before the Q&A. These people don't necessarily need full access to the protectee. Still, they'll need temporary access at some point during the event. In other words, they'd have limited access.

The last category is the one that gets a little touchy. If someone is granted access but displays threatening behavior (physically or verbally), agents must quickly revoke access to keep the protectee safe.

There's more to access control than just the name checks and magnetometers. There is door and window access to consider to secure the protectee's specific travel path throughout the venue. The advance team puts in many necessary hours preparing for the protectee's arrival.

HOW DOES THIS APPLY TO YOU?

For the next couple of days, you'll be taking an extensive hard look at who and what controls your daily actions and emotions right now. Who currently has access to your life, and are there areas where changes are needed for you to protect you and your desired legacy? Essentially, you'll be looking at your access control through a Secret Service mindset.

Today, though, you will make some lists to get started.

Let's look at a basic protection diagram. In the luncheon scenario laid out previously, the advance agents would create site diagrams showing the protectee's path of travel and the locations of notable things like bathrooms and exits.

For your protection plan, we'll start with a basic template like this:

BASIC PROTECTION DIAGRAM

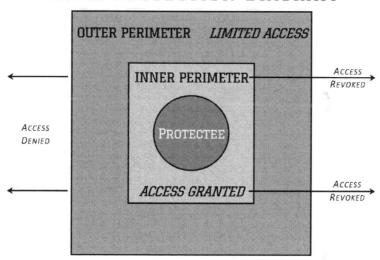

In your personal protection advance assignment, you're the protectee, and there's an inner and outer perimeter around you. The inner perimeter occupants have full access granted. The outer perimeter occupants are those with limited access. Everyone else has access denied or had their access revoked.

Now let's get to your advance work for the day.

TODAY'S ADVANCE WORK:

WRITE IT DOWN...

MAKE A LIST OF THE PEOPLE YOU SEE WITHIN ANY GIVEN WEEK.

Examples: Family Members, Close Friends, Classmates, Coaches, Teammates, Teachers, etc.

_____

_____

_____

_____

_____

_____

_____

_____

_____

_____

_____

TODAY'S ADVANCE WORK:

WRITE IT DOWN...

WHAT WEBSITES DO YOU VISIT DAILY?

Examples: Blogs, Social Media, Email, etc.

TODAY'S ADVANCE WORK:

WRITE IT DOWN...

LIST THE LOCATIONS YOU VISIT REGULARLY DURING ANY GIVEN WEEK.

Examples: School, Home, Relative or Friends House, Church, Practice, Tutoring, etc.

_____

_____

_____

_____

_____

_____

_____

_____

_____

_____

_____

Congratulations, my friend! You just made your version of a "name-checks" list. We will tackle the "screening" process starting tomorrow. Keep adding names, places, and sites to your list as they pop up throughout the day. I know the lists might get long. That's okay. You don't need to include everyone in every class. You should include people like your lab partner and your group project members. Focus on the people you come in closer contact with every day.

We're just getting started with your advance work. You're doing great! Keep going!

REMINDER

"Only make decisions that support your self-image, self-esteem, and self worth."

Oprah Winfrey

DAY 3:

INTERNAL
ACCESS
CONTROL

Access control can be broken down into two categories: outer (or physical) access control and inner (or emotional) access control. There might be some overlap, but I'll separate them for now.

For this workbook, outer access control is physical protection and the steps involved in keeping yourself physically safe. It ranges from proactive protection like securing access points to your home (locking doors and windows) to preparing for reactive protection like taking a self-defense class if you ever have to engage with an attacker.

Internal access control is about protecting who and what is allowed to control our thoughts, emotions, feelings, and actions. This one is less straightforward than physical protection because someone (like social media) can access you emotionally without necessarily having accessed you physically.

Today's focus is on internal access control.

For me, protecting myself on the inside is one of the most complex parts of self-care. I can be a people pleaser. I can get caught up in trying to be accommodating and nonconfrontational. In the past, I prided myself in being "laid-back" and "non-high-maintenance," as if those qualities made me more fun to be around and a better person in general.

19

Always going with the flow never made me a better person. It took me over three decades to get that through my thick head, but I'm finally at the point in my life where I don't want to be like everyone else. I don't have to be invisible to be tolerated or liked, and I don't care if I'm controversial sometimes.

Most of us can do better at protecting our legacies and ourselves, but all too often outside influences are allowed to stifle personal growth. Being rebelliously outspoken about living meaningfully and protecting myself has cost me some long-time "friends" who proved they were not friends in the first place.

When I stood up for myself, I was called "selfish" by a controlling friend I'd known since before high school. Unfortunately, I also don't have a relationship with some of my extended family members. It's unfortunate, and navigating familial boundaries is excruciating sometimes.

There is an inevitable loss associated with inner protection. I can't sugarcoat that for you. I'd be doing you a disservice if I did.

I believe it's easy to stay miserable in a toxic situation because it's familiar. Assertive change is terrifying. There's no other fancy way to put it.

However, the beautiful outcome of revoking access to my life's toxic aspects was additional room for positive additions to my inner circle. Withdrawal is typically my answer to emotional hurt. Revoking access to everyone means I can't get hurt again, right? That's my pain talking, but it's no way to live long-term.

There's a difference between stepping back to heal and wallowing in solitude to protect me. Stepping away from the toxic helped me be more aware of how daily influences affect me. I realized I had amazing people and opportunities in front of me if I could respect myself enough to declutter my inner circle positively.

Yesterday's advance work involved making lists. Today's advance work will include questions about the contents of your lists. The questions are not all-encompassing or the only ones you could ask yourself in your specific situations. Nonetheless, they should help you thoughtfully consider where the contents of your lists fall within your access points.

REMEMBER

People are more than
just part of a list

I have one word of caution about your lists. Categorizing people into toxic versus nontoxic categories can be a slippery slope. These lists are merely tools to get you thinking. The focus is not necessarily on the list itself; it's how the lists' contents affect you.

After all, you are the protectee and the protector. Look at these lists with the mindset of a protector. If these lists belonged to someone else— knowing what you know about the relationships associated with them— what insight would you have about these lists? Give the protectee (you) thoughtful attention.

At a minimum, there's probably someone you've allowed into your inner circle who needs to be limited to the outer perimeter of your security plan. There's probably someone with restricted access to you because you don't like that this person pushes you to be better and do better.

When I was going through my divorce, I had an eating disorder relapse. My compulsive exercising, intermittent bulimia, and restrictive eating got out of hand as I struggled through some emotional life changes. I saw an eating disorder specialist who wasn't afraid to call me out, and I didn't like it because she was right. Sometimes I canceled sessions with her because I didn't want my dysfunction to be challenged and didn't feel ready to make any positive changes.

During one of our sessions, she told me I was quite a rebellious soul. I couldn't see it. I was too fixated on my skewed idea of perfection. At the end of our session, she said, "Melanie, you're a rebel. Maybe if you'd just break the rules once in a while, you'd start seeing your beautiful self and embrace who she wants to be. Be okay with the fact that she isn't going to be perfect."

Sigh. *Yeah, I needed that.* Maybe you can relate to my scenario somewhere in your life too. You don't have to be like everyone else, and being uncommon or unique is some to own with pride, not hide wish shame.

All right, take a deep breath, look through yesterday's "name-checks" lists, and ponder some "screening" questions. If you need to take a break, that's okay. If you're rushing, maybe you're avoiding something. Take your time.

HOW DO I FEEL WHEN I'M AROUND THIS PERSON OR PLACE?

Examples: Does a friend belittle you when you are successful? Does your significant other pressure you to change to fit a preference? Perhaps someone on your list makes you feel convicted and challenged. This is not always a bad thing. Are you revoking access because you are too proud to admit they push you to be better?

What about places? Can you think of a location that brings you joy and leaves you feeling fulfilled? Is there a way to add more of this place to your life? Is there a club or sport you've been part of for a long time that no longer interests you?

It's one thing to be committed and another to be burned out. I've learned that some sports, clubs, and jobs are meant to be for a season. It's not quitting to move forward productively and positively. Only you can determine your real motives. But if something is coming to mind as you read this, take time to hash it out with yourself inwardly.

WHAT DOES THIS PERSON OR PLACE ADD TO MY LIFE?

Everything in your lists will add something to your life. It might be joy, laughter, productivity, education, etc. On the flip side, some of your lists might be a source of stress, anger, resentment, and even abuse.

There might even be items on your lists that might add distractions. Perhaps there's a way to limit its control on your time and energy.

If something is coming to mind, don't ignore it.

DO I ALTER MY ACTIONS WHEN I'M AROUND THIS PERSON? IF SO, IS IT POSITIVELY OR NEGATIVELY?

Have you noticed that you behave differently around certain people? I'm not talking about situations like being professional at a job versus goofing off with friends. Of course, there's a time for professionalism and a time to relax and be silly. Both can be done authentically.

Sometimes we allow someone to stifle our true selves for one reason or another. Do you allow someone to silence you while others make it easy for your voice to be heard? Do you alter your appearance for acceptance or popularity?

When I first started speaking about my time with the Secret Service and how necessary self-protection had become to me, I worried about what I "should" wear on stage. As a Secret Service agent, I always wore plain business suits and collared shirts. There's wasn't a lot of room for workplace fashion, if you know what I mean. To me, a professional speaking gig probably warranted business attire: slacks, fancy shirts, heels, etc. I figured that would make people take me seriously. Look the part, and they'll listen to me.

But how is that being true to myself? I altered my actions and changed who I wanted to be to fit what I thought people around me would respect. But guess what? Do you know how freeing it was to show up at a speaking gig for a young women's leadership seminar in wedge sneakers? (I don't even care if they're not "in style" anymore. I love those shoes!)

Debating an outfit might seem like a trivial example here, but the point is this: if someone or something in your life feels like it's forcing you to be someone you're not, then that access to you needs to be addressed.

Own who you are, what you love, and who you want to be! It feels so good when you do! Don't let harmful access stifle your beautiful self.

DOES SOCIAL MEDIA'S PRESENCE OR ABSENCE AFFECT YOUR MOOD OR DEMEANOR?

Okay, this is a big one for me. I recently looked at my screen time stats on my phone, and it was embarrassing how much time I was spending on social media. Let's just say it was way too much time mindlessly scrolling. What a waste of time I'll never get back, procrastination at its finest. I turned off almost all of my social media notifications after a while, which helped me avoid constant distractions.

There's a lot of talk about how social media and unrealistic filters damage people's self-esteem and mental health. I think I am influenced by social media more than I want to admit. I allow social media to enslave me to comparison sometimes, and that, quite obviously, shows me that it needs to be limited in my life.

I used to be obsessed with buying tabloid-esque magazines when I checked out at the grocery store. I called them my "gossip and sleaze" fix to remind me that my life wasn't as messed up as some rich celebrities. (I know. I cringed when I admitted it, too.)

But what I was doing was a lot of body comparisons because of my eating disorder history. I wanted to be as thin as a movie star. I wanted to look like the models. Nothing about reading those magazines helped me, and I saved a lot of money when I bypassed them at the grocery store indefinitely.

Are you obsessed with likes and follower counts? Do you delete content when it isn't as popular as you hoped? Do you limit yourself only to posting content you know will be popular? If so, are you compromising yourself or exposing yourself for the popularity of strangers?

I'm not saying you have to get rid of social media entirely if your screen time is high. I'm saying if your mood deteriorates when social media doesn't meet your validation needs, then perhaps there's an access control problem. That kind of distraction probably isn't going anywhere healthy.

IF I'M HONEST WITH MYSELF, WHO OR WHAT CONTROLS ME THE MOST?

My answer to this one has changed over the years. Back in high school and college, I allowed my eating disorder to control my daily thoughts and actions. Romantic relationships (or the desire for one) dominated my mind for a while.

After college, I allowed work to control me most of the time. I said "yes" to work and "no" to myself and my loved ones. Granting control to a job was ultimately a severe sign of personal neglect.

The Secret Service could replace me in a second. I didn't realize my ego was getting in the way of proper access control. I convinced myself that the job wouldn't get done if I weren't at work. My employers even alluded to that fact, and I bought into that thought process for years. I didn't take vacation time. I went to work when I was sick. I wish I saw this toxic access control issue sooner because my employers didn't care about me. They just didn't want to be inconvenienced.

Today, imposter syndrome creeps in if I'm not careful. I think I'm not qualified to speak on self-protection because I still struggle with it daily. I know we all have a story (and a story worth telling) and that my learning might be helpful and motivating to others. But there's always that little voice in my head that says I'm not good enough or intelligent enough to think I have something of value to offer.

Access control is usually a choice. I realize I need to fill my life with people and places that magnify the legacy I want. I also know I'm a better person when choosing legacy-based access control.

Your turn. Who or what controls you the most?

HOW CAN I PROACTIVELY GRANT ACCESS TO SOMEONE OR SOMETHING POSITIVE?

I think this is a compelling and potentially life-changing question. Has a name kept creeping into your mind as you're reflecting today? Think about what interests you. If you love animals, perhaps you could reach out to your local shelters. Maybe they have an event coming up and could use your help, or maybe they're looking for people to walk the rescue dogs. This could potentially be a proactive way to add something positive to your life by replacing something time-sucking and negative. Just an idea, but you get the point.

FINISHING UP
TODAY'S ADVANCE WORK

When you're ready, turn to the next page and write down some scenarios you know you need to address.

TODAY'S ADVANCE WORK:

NOW LET'S GET REAL...

Use this space to journal or reflect on the lists you made yesterday.
How is your access control?
Give yourself some time to reflect. Are you seeing any potential
red flags you might need to address?
You've got this!

_____

_____

_____

_____

_____

_____

_____

_____

_____

_____

Finish today on a positive note! Did today's reflection bring someone or something positive to your attention? Celebrate and appreciate this new realization and write it down with gratitude.

TODAY'S
POSITIVE ACCESS
HIGHLIGHTS

Access control is recognizing who and what are allowed to control and influence your daily thoughts and actions and doing something about it when needed.

You are worth protecting.

DAY 4:

PHYSICAL
ACCESS
CONTROL

Today is all about physical protection. And guess what? You don't have to be a ninja to start protecting yourself a little better starting today. There are small, thoughtful steps and habits that can help keep you safe. Let's get started.

Personal protection can be proactive or reactive. Proactive protection involves taking steps today to avoid potential security problems. Reactive protection happens when security is compromised, and you have to face a potential attacker or hostile situation. You can prepare for reactive protection with proactive practice!

Now let's break it down some more. I like to look at proactive protection into three basic steps: awareness, access, and intuition.

PROACTIVE PROTECTION

1. **Awareness Always**
2. **Monitor Access Control**
3. **Trust Your Intuition**

Now let's look at each one individually.

AWARENESS
"HEAD ON A SWIVEL"
The more you pay attention to the mundane everyday things, the more likely you are to spot the abnormal when it counts.

When I was an agent, we were constantly reminded to keep our heads on a swivel, meaning we should stay vigilant when scanning our surroundings and spot potential problems. For example, let's say I was assigned to a presidential campaign speech, and my post was near the stage. I'd scan the crowd for anything potentially abnormal or suspicious. Campaign speeches are often open to the general public, and the groups can be considerable.

For example, if someone in the crowd is wearing a bulky winter coat in the middle of summer, that would be a red flag. A person can conceal a lot in a coat, and its presence is out-of-place in the first place. In this case, agents would need to further assess this person and situation.

When I think about situational awareness, I like to think of it as a combination of Secret Service awareness and my nosy great-grandma's awareness of her neighbors. My great-grandma used to sit and look out her kitchen window with binoculars. There was probably no one on the block more aware of the neighborhood's regular comings and goings. (Stick with me. I know that's a little creepy.)

It helps me to think like a Secret Service agent when I'm in public and to know what my great-grandma knew when I'm at home.

HOW TO THINK LIKE A SECRET SERVICE AGENT IN PUBLIC

When I go into a public place, I tell myself to cover my bases. Not to overanalyze the baseball analogy, but in baseball, the term "cover the bases" refers to infielders proactively preparing to receive the ball at their bases. For instance, if there's an opposing player on second base, the third baseman might move closer to the base since the opposing player will probably be heading in that direction. In other words, covering the bases is a proactive movement to be in the right place when it counts.

You can cover your "bases" in public as a proactive habit, and you can remember how to do it by remembering the acronym B-A-S-E-S.

COVER THE BASES
OBSERVATIONS IN PUBLIC

B - Behavior
A - Access Points
S - Security
E - Exterior Locations
S - Safeguards

BEHAVIOR

As you make your way through a public place, practice listening and observing what's around you. Do the conversations appear pleasant or aggressive? Do employees or staff members appear on edge? Is anyone behaving abnormally for the location?

For example, if you're at a grocery store and see the same person multiple times throughout the store, it might be a coincidence. But if this person is not pushing a cart, selecting items, or doesn't appear to be shopping at all, this behavior might cause concern.

If you're feeling uncomfortable, there's probably a reason. It might be a good idea to either seek help or remove yourself from the situation.

ACCESS POINTS

When you enter a public place, note how the area is accessed (doors, escalators, elevators, etc.) In the event of an emergency, you've already been observant and will probably respond quickly and more accurately.

For example, when you enter a restaurant, look around as you wait to be seated. Can you spot other doors as well as the kitchen entrance? Most restaurants have a back door within the kitchen area. Doors marked as emergency exits are generally locked from the outside and are strictly for egress purposes.

A good rule of thumb is to never sit with your back to the door.

SECURITY

Does the facility have police presence or security on site? If the venue uses private security, take note of the uniform color so you can spot them quickly if needed. Another location to note is the security office, a good meeting place if you or members of your group become separated.

For example, professional sporting events typically have private security and police presence. If the security office location isn't marked or recognizable, ask a staff member or security officer. Perhaps a public phone number exists to contact a dispatch office. Access to this information may be helpful if a rowdy crowd turns disruptive or dangerous.

EXTERIOR LOCATIONS

I have a terrible natural sense of direction. It's gotten slightly better over the years, but I got lost a lot when I was in high school and college. I've had to work at being better at my directional awareness.

Directional awareness can be hard to maintain indoors, especially in places like shopping malls or hotels with multiple hallways and turns throughout. However, it's a good habit to have a general sense of where you are within a building.

Do you know where you parked in relation to where your hotel room is located? When you sit down at a restaurant, did you notice the police station across the street? These are few examples, but it's worth noting in the event of an emergency requiring you to leave a public place quickly.

SAFEGUARDS

Safeguards are things that might keep you safe or help you create distance between you and a potential attacker. When I took Krav Maga classes (an Israeli martial art), the instructors often talked about looking for the "weapons at your disposal."

Not everything is an obvious weapon, of course, but if you're out on a hike, a rock can be a weapon that's thrown at an aggressor or attacker. If you're at a restaurant, a lamp or other décor can be used as a means to ward off an attacker. Large furniture pieces can be moved in front of a door quickly or create a barrier between you and an attacker.

Identifying safeguards is being aware, not afraid. Hopefully, you never have to use these weapons at your disposal. But knowing they're there is part of being aware. Can you think of any other possible safeguards?

HOW TO BE "GREAT-GRANDMA AWARE" AT HOME

When you're at home, you're in a familiar place. I can pretty much navigate my home in the dark because I know where the doorways are and pass through them regularly. You probably can do the same at your residence, too.

But how much do you know about your home and your neighborhood? If you recently moved, this part of your advance work is important because some things are probably still unfamiliar.

My great-grandma knew everything about her neighbors' daily activities and events on her street. She knew everyone's cars, work schedules, bus schedules, etc. If something were out of place or amiss, she'd know it.

If something were amiss on your block, would you notice? Are you familiar enough with your surroundings to recognize an unfamiliar car circling the block? Maybe you're not close with your neighbors, and that's okay. But are they familiar to you?

I had a neighbor who suddenly stopped going to work, and I didn't see her husband for a couple of weeks. There was a snowstorm one night, and the following day I went out to shovel the snow. I'm not too fond of that chore, but I did both sides since I shared a driveway with my neighbors.

I got a text from my neighbor that day thanking me. Her husband was in the hospital, and she was anxious about getting out of her driveway to see him. I don't think I would have done their side of the driveway had I not observed that their movements had changed a lot. It was an excellent reminder to check on my neighbors sooner when something seems off.

You never know what people are dealing with behind closed doors sometimes.

Today is a great day to start being more aware of what happens outside your house. You don't have to go buy some binoculars and be "that" creepy neighbor.

The more you're aware of the familiar, the more likely you recognize the unfamiliar when it counts.

REMINDER

**Know what's up
on your block**

ACCESS CONTROL

**It's not about keeping
everyone out. It's about
being proactive and smart
about who gets close and
recognizing when you might
need to be reactive.**

I know access control is a recurring theme, but here we go again. Let's look at your home. There are probably multiple ways to access your home or apartment building. Doors, windows, garages, elevators, and stairwells are all possibilities.

First things first, if you live with other people, it's essential you're all on the same page when it comes to securing your home. Have a conversation about boundaries and how you'll collectively address how your home is accessed.

When I was in college, I lived on campus. Dorms and campus apartments get a lot of traffic. Some students left their doors unlocked all the time. But my roommate and I didn't like the idea of it being okay for people to walk in to visit whenever they wanted. We set a boundary together early on. When we weren't home, we locked the door. And if we were busy with schoolwork, we locked the door, recognizing that we were not obligated to answer the door just because someone knocked.

I am someone who values and respects my space. I like the idea of home being a haven that can be a secure place when I need space.

Remember, you are not obligated to grant access to anyone who makes you feel uncomfortable. We are taught to be polite and kind to everyone, but you (and I) might feel hesitate to speak up at times. But at the end of the day, you do not have to be polite to someone who is, for example, being excessively flirty and flirtatious despite your rejections. You do not have to answer personal questions from strangers if you don't want to. You do not have to disclose or expose yourself because someone makes you feel they're entitled to access.

Manners and politeness don't always belong in a situation with negative access attempts.

TODAY'S ADVANCE WORK:

WHEN YOU ENTER A PUBLIC PLACE TODAY, COVER YOUR BASES.

What did you see?

_____

_____

_____

_____

_____

_____

_____

_____

_____

_____

_____

HOME ACCESS CONTROL

BEST PRACTICES

- Know who has access to keys (if you've recently moved, change the locks and ask your landlord about it if renting)
- Talk to roommates about locking doors and what works for fellow residents
- Do all doors and windows have functioning locks? (Speak to your landlord about having them fixed if you don't own the place)
- Consider installing cameras or a security system (doorbell camera, hallway camera, etc.)

HOW CAN YOU BETTER SECURE YOUR HOME AND CREATE PROTECTIVE HABITS WITHIN YOUR HOUSEHOLD?

WHAT'S YOUR PLAN?

_____

_____

_____

_____

_____

PHYSICAL PROTECTION: FIGHT, FLIGHT, OR FREEZE?

There's a lot to consider when it comes to self-defense, and it can be intimidating. There are so many different martial arts styles, self-defense gadgets, and experts in the field. Self-defense is part of proactive preparation for reactive protection. If you had to fight someone trying to harm you, reacting quickly could be the difference between remaining safe or something worse. If you haven't practiced, how will you know how you could respond to protect yourself best?

When I first started the Secret Service Academy, I'd never been in a fight in my life. I'd never been punched or had to defend myself physically. But I learned something quickly. When I took my first hit in a training environment, I fought back. Poorly, I might add. But I fought back. I had a lot to learn, and I'm pretty sure I was the brunt of a few jokes based on my initial "fight."

Generally speaking, when you feel threatened, you'll respond in one of three ways: fight, flight, or freeze. Freezing probably won't do you any good. If you're able to get away (flight), that's usually ideal. But, if the situation goes a different way, fighting, while not perfect, might be necessary.

FRIENDLY REMINDER

You have a right to protect yourself, and you are worth protecting.

Here are a few things to keep in mind regarding physical protection. These, as always, are not all-encompassing, and you should be proactive with educating yourself and practicing beyond these pages. Research local self-defense classes, for example. Many communities offer these for free.

IF YOU'RE BEING
THREATENED

- Make noise
  - Call for help to draw attention to yourself
- Create distance between you and the potential attacker
  - Use weapons at your disposal
- If you have to fight, fight with all your might
  - Proactive preparation

SAMPLE "WEAPONS" AT YOUR
DISPOSAL

- Keys
- Purse
- Rocks
- Furniture
- Self-defense keychain
- Décor items such as vases
- Frying pan
- Broom (or other long object to create distance)
- Anything else come to mind?

Here's your last piece of advance work for today:

TODAY'S ADVANCE WORK:

RESEARCH SOME WAYS TO EDUCATE YOURSELF ABOUT PHYSICAL PROTECTION, LEARN NEW SKILLS, AND PRACTICE WHAT YOU LEARNED.

What did you find?

_____

_____

_____

_____

_____

_____

_____

_____

_____

_____

_____

And, finally, I'll leave you with this piece of advice when it comes to intuition and protecting yourself. An instructor at the Secret Service academy said this once, and I don't think I can put it any better.

INTUITION

"TRUST YOUR GUT"

**If something doesn't look right, smell right, or simply doesn't feel right, then don't ignore it.
It probably isn't right.**

REMINDER

Your motto for self-protection should be one of preparation, not fear.

Prepared, not scared!

DAY 5:

SITUATION REPORTS

Yesterday was a lot, I know. Today will deal with some heavy "stuff" that might be tough. You're going to give yourself a situation report.

The Secret Service provides periodic situation reports during protection assignments. They're a status update. When a motorcade is on the way to an event, the destination's agents regularly communicate with the motorcade about the event. For instance, if a demonstration pops up, that would be something to include. Crowd size and other pertinent information need to be accurately relayed so everyone is informed by the time of arrival.

If an agent gives an inaccurate situation report, there could be problems. If, for example, a catering truck pulls up to the wrong entrance and blocks the motorcade's arrival point, the agent needs to call that out on the radio immediately so everyone can react appropriately and avoid an issue.

But what about the situation reports we give ourselves about how we're doing?

When my marriage ended, I handled it poorly (to put it mildly). I had been unhappy for a long time, but it didn't affect my work because I suppressed my feelings when I walked into work. It was easier to keep everything buried after work too.

But when I had to face the fact that my marriage was in deep trouble, it became harder to keep the hurt and sadness from bubbling to the surface. It didn't take long for me to have a hard time getting out of bed in the morning.

When I got hired at the Secret Service, they told me about the Employee Assistance Program (EAP). I probably got a pamphlet about it at some point, and I'm sure the break rooms had posters with a telephone number to call if anyone needed help.

My ego thought I had it together. I wouldn't need an assistance program. I could deal with my problems on my own.

Oh, I was wrong.

Looking back, one of the strongest moments of my life was the day I called the EAP number and admitted I needed help. I was so afraid of being judged by a male-dominated employer of tough people. I never wanted to appear weak, so I forced myself to be strong even when my personal life needed serious work. But I didn't feel judged. In fact, within just a couple of days, the people at the EAP had several counselors ready to meet with me.

That phone call was a big turning point for me. I needed to get help.

I got help. My marriage still ended. I was still diagnosed with depression. I still struggled.

I think it's important to remember this:

You can revoke access to the things that bring you down, but real change won't start until you address what's going on inside.

I thought my troubles would be gone once the major stressors were removed (toxic marriage and work environment). I thought I was free from the negative, and I got complacent. Shortly after the divorce was final, I left the Secret Service and moved into a tiny apartment in Los Angeles. Within just a couple of days, the past came bubbling up to the surface, and I allowed myself to get into a low place. I contemplated the idea of not living anymore, and I'm thankful I didn't go through with it. My dog started flipping out when I was falling apart that night, and she brought me back to reality. I was scared of my dark thoughts.

I had to ask for help again. I had to give myself an honest situation report. In the Secret Service, situation reports need to end with "all clear for arrival" so the motorcade knows that everything is under control.

Sometimes I'm not "all clear," and I can't tell myself I'm fine when it comes to personal status updates. I might have to ask for help again in the future, too. Situation reports are like asking yourself, "How are you?" and forcing yourself to avoid the default answer of "I'm fine" when you're not.

Going through this workbook and reflecting on your life might not be enough. Trauma can be rough. I haven't even touched on some of the heavier topics where access is forcefully made in abuse, assault, rape, etc.

I am not a psychologist or a mental health specialist in any form. I can't give you the tools to process and overcome tragedies like these, but there are excellent professionals out there who can help.

I understand not everyone has access to an Employee Assistance Program like I did. But some people can point you in the right direction if you ask.

PEOPLE TO ASK FOR

HELP

School Counselor, a Trusted Teacher, Doctor, Police, Parents, Mentor, Coach, Neighbor, Mental Health Hotlines, Supervisor, etc.

Can you think of any other options that apply
to you?

*There are people who can point you in the
right direction if you need help.*

When it comes to living with depression and being mindful of it daily, I've learned that legacy, access control, and situation reports are all connected. When my situation report isn't all clear, my access control usually has some problems. And when both of those are off track, I've typically lost sight of my legacy and self-respect.

It helps me to revert to my legacy and remind myself of who and what I am protecting in the first place. The access control problems become more evident when I remember the big picture: I want to be the best Melanie Lentz I can be and live the most meaningful life of love I can live. What's keeping me from that today? What small step can I take right now to refocus and move forward?

Situation reports have become a daily thing for me. I lie to myself sometimes. I admit it. I think I'm tough some days or that I need to "suck it up" all of the time. Yes, there are times when I need to focus on a task or assignment and do my job. But I have learned (the hard way) that when the first opportunity presents itself, I need to take a deep breath and say, "Mel, what's your situation report, and what are you going to do about it?"

I (try) to maintain a long-term focus (legacy) with short-term steps in a positive direction. Checking in with myself like a situation report makes this long-term focus applicable daily.

Today's advance work is giving yourself an honest situation report. If you're "all clear," then that's awesome! Keep moving forward. But don't make this your only situation report. Life is unpredictable, and there will be a day when you're not clear and need to act. Those are hard days, but coping with them in healthy ways might involve reaching outside yourself for help. Remember, there is absolutely no shame in that.

If you think you might need to get some help based on your current circumstances, it can't hurt to ask someone you trust to point you in the right direction. It's better to ask for help. I know it's not the easiest thing to do, but I encourage you always to keep the option open for the day you need help.

TODAY'S
SITUATION
REPORT

DAY 6:

AWARENESS
OF OTHERS

Today, I'm going to flip things around and ask you a question:

Look back at your access control lists from Day Two of this workbook. If those people were looking at your name on their list, would they need to limit or revoke access to you for negative reasons?

Think about that question for a bit. When I think about it, I can always think of an instance when my recent behavior did not reflect the person I want to be. Maybe I treated someone poorly because I was having a bad day. Perhaps I snapped at a loved one because I was stressed about something unrelated to them. Maybe I blew off a friend who needed a friend at the moment because I just wanted to be alone in my problems.

How I treat people daily says a lot about me. I don't think we realize how powerful one interaction can be. One hurtful or dismissive comment, one insecure and spiteful piece of gossip, and even one moment spent ignoring another person's existence can have an impact on someone's life long after the moment has passed.

I struggle the most with the way other women treat each other sometimes. I've had many "mean girls" in my life over the years. It makes me sad because, even though I'm in my thirties now, women still act like children to one another.

I wrote a blog on my website after some "mean girl" interactions. I was thinking about what my role (if any) would be in a mean girl's life. Here are my (unedited) thoughts from that blog:

"Getting a Life"

www.melanielentz.com/badblogging/meangirls

The hashtag #womenempoweringwomen has over 2.2 million posts on Instagram alone right now. It's 2020, and one can't turn on the television or scroll social media for very long without coming across something pertaining to women's rights, equality, and empowerment.

But, alas, sometimes women are still mean to each other.

When girls were mean to me when I was younger, my dad would say, "Just kill them with kindness."

My mom would say, "You just be your kind self and don't worry about them."

Friends would say, "She's just jealous of you. Ignore her."

Growing up, I wanted to be liked. I never wanted to cause a problem. I wanted everyone around me to be happy. Everyone has their bad moments, but I'd like to think I was mostly viewed as a nice person. But even nice people deal with mean people. It always bothered me when I wasn't liked or other girls were mean or tried to sabotage me with classic mean girl tactics.

I try not to give people a reason to dislike me. That much hasn't changed for as long as I can remember.

I thought women would change as I got older, that mean girls would also grow up and mature alongside me. They'd get over their insecurities and their meanness would dissolve.

Well, THAT was all false.

I'm tired of being nice to mean girls. I recognize that this is a very "human" statement, but I'm just being honest. I feel bad just typing it. Sometimes mean people can be the worst when it comes to affecting my attitude.

I always say it doesn't take much effort to be a decent person, but sometimes it takes a little extra willpower to remain nice when the behavior isn't reciprocated. Being nice to mean people can be draining, at least it is for me. People wonder why public service employees like police officers and nurses get jaded over time. Maybe it's because no matter how much good they try to do and the help they try to provide, there's always one more bad interaction to ruin good intentions.

I've been thinking a lot about how to deal with mean girls. It seems like they keep popping up from time to time. Mean girls used to bother me a lot, and I would internalize those underlying rejection feelings. I've matured in that regard over the years. One person's acceptance adds no additional value to my worth as a person, so why bother stewing about it when they don't like me? Don't get me wrong; the initial sting is still there. I am just able to recognize it before I get too much into my head about it.

A week or two ago, I went out of my way to do something nice for a woman I know doesn't like me. She's told others she doesn't like me, and her "reasons" were vague and trivial. If I didn't know better, I'd say she hates me (and that's a strong word). The specifics don't matter, but she rolled her eyes at me and refused my kind gesture, making me want to give up and just ignore her until the end of time.

I was ready to scream, "ENOUGH WITH THE MEAN GIRL CRAP!" What really is so terrible about me in your eyes? It's 2020. Women are all about empowering each other. It's cool to be empowering. It's trendy to #womenempoweringwomen.

More importantly, empowering and encouraging each other positively is the RIGHT thing to do.

When I first got out of the Secret Service Academy, I experienced my first mean girl interaction on the job. I was twenty-three and still learning to navigate a big girl job in a "man's world." Another younger female agent decided she didn't like me from the get-go, and she and I eventually exchanged words at a hotel during a campaign assignment in Kansas City. Many in the group had been drinking during dinner, so I was driving the rental van back to the hotel since I didn't drink.

She sat in the back seat, making rude comments about me the whole way back to the hotel (and not in a whisper so I wouldn't hear). I'd had enough by the time we got back, and we lashed out at each other. Later that night, I reached out and asked to talk. I thought we worked things out. I distinctly remember saying, "You were also hired young like me. I'm still figuring things out. I don't understand why you and I can't be there for each other and help each other."

I thought we were fine. We were never friends, but we were civil. All good, right?

Fast forward ten years (yes, ten years), and I ran into her in New York City while visiting another Secret Service friend. She looked at me, I smiled at her, and she gave me a dirty look and turned toward my friend as if I didn't exist. My friend, who was in the other rental van on the Kansas City trip, was aware of what had happened years before and commented on how awkward that was that she pretended I was invisible for the whole conversation.

"It's pretty sad that ten years later, she couldn't just say hello and move on with life."

But I didn't lose a second of sleep over it. I wasn't the one who made that awkward. What has to be going through a woman's mind when she decides to be that way? Probably more than I realize, and it probably has absolutely nothing to do with me in the end.

I won't go on and on with every instance of mean girl-ness in my past or present. But the sheer volume of it, especially as I'm getting older, is saddening today more than it is irritating.

So... here is the question I think needs addressing in my life:

WHAT ROLE DOES A MEAN GIRL PLAY IN MY LIFE?

It's like the Secret Service concept of access control I tout so much. A strong woman must know when another person should have access granted into her life, when access should be denied, when access should be revoked, and when access should be limited.

Here's my blunt answer to my question:

A mean girl should not have a role in my life.

Why? Her criticism is ill-intentioned and not constructive. She doesn't point out my mistakes or flaws with the attitude of "I know you can do better, and I'm right here to encourage you while we figure our own stuff out." She doesn't offer a solution or assistance. She's the demolition woman rather than a rebuilding team. When I'm broken like any other woman, she doesn't come with a hammer and nails to help put things together. She swings the hammer, and I have to dodge its blow lest she change me negatively with some new and unimproved rough edges.

There are times when I can't avoid a mean girl physically. Sometimes she's a coworker or someone I have to interact with professionally at some point. But I can avoid giving her access to my sense of self-worth. I can revoke her role in my life if I've let her in before. I can rebuild myself and get better despite her. That inner growth makes it easier to keep her and her negativity out of my thoughts and feelings about myself.

The more I think about it, the more I feel like I might need to flip things around, though.

Here's my second, and probably more important, question:

WHAT IS MY ROLE, IF ANY, IN A MEAN GIRL'S LIFE?

Here's what I know:

1. My role in a woman's life is NEVER to bring her down or make her feel bad about herself.

2. There will be women in my life who will not be there for a positive experience.

3. I must embrace, appreciate, uplift, and grant access to the women who ARE uplifting and examples of positive relationships.

My role in a mean girl's life is merely a circumstantial opportunity for kindness. It is possible to be the bigger person and have self-respect at the same time. I establish the boundaries between us, and I need to recognize that not every woman will be a positive and empowering presence. Not every woman will treat me the way I want to be treated or the way I treat them.

But, regardless, here's the kind of woman I want to be.

I want to be the woman the mean girl knows she could come to in a tough time, and I'd be the first to give her a hug. I also want to be the woman with enough good sense and self-respect to expect nothing in return.

My role in her life is to be what she is not to me.

My role in her life is to build her up when I can and continue on with my life. My role is to protect myself while providing a layer of love and protection to others whenever possible.

Sometimes I'm just not liked for my style of humanness. I'm not enough for some. I'm too much for others.

The women who should have more of a role in my life are the ones who encourage my style of humanness to be authentic and heard because I DO have something to offer despite my incredibly flawed humanness. I can be meaningful despite it.

For example, last week, a female executive offered to help me with my keynotes and pointed out a correction that needed to be made to my website. In the same week, another female told me to "get a life" with a public comment on last week's blog.

Which woman is genuinely demonstrating empowerment? The answer should be obvious.

I read once that we can all learn from criticism if we can take what's constructive from it. It's hard for me to find anything constructive in the blog comment. If I reach a little bit (a lot), get a life isn't bad advice, I suppose. I already have a life, though. In fact, I keep trying to be better throughout it. I do that by reflecting and learning from my experiences, and I'll continue to "seriously" blog about whatever the hell I want because I don't write to impress people and win their favor. I want to move them and make them think inwardly because that's where change really starts.

I want to be part of the change, and I'll always have inward work to do. You don't have to read about it on Monday's if you don't want to. I'll be okay because I'm learning to welcome the positive relationships rather than shut everyone out because of a few mean girls.

Today, pay attention to the interactions you have with other people. Tomorrow, do the same. Be mindful of how your presence (access) in others' lives makes them feel. Keep doing it. Your company in this world is powerful, and ten seconds of small kindnesses or negativities last much longer than the time you spent on them.

Let's end today on a positive note. You're amazing. (Just wanted to remind you of that again.)

HOW I DEMONSTRATED
POSITIVE ACCESS
TO SOMEONE ELSE TODAY

REMINDER

**Be the kind of person
you need today.**

Remember Your Legacy

DAY 7:

APPLICATION

You made it! Day Seven is here! Today is a day of application. You've spent the last week identifying ways to protect yourself better, inside and out. You've just scratched the surface. Physical protection could be a book all by itself.

I hope that the last week made you think. I hope you'll continue to build on the basics we've covered this week. I am still learning and growing and will be for the rest of my life. I know what happens when I lose my way, and I don't want to go back there and repeat history.

Advance work is never done, but it gets better with time.

Every day I wake up and choose to remember who I want to be. Some days I know I'm not a source of positive access to others. We all have bad days. But a bad day doesn't mean I've failed at life. Whenever I have a terrible day, I joke that I need to try again tomorrow. I know I can never stop trying. Despite all of the "plot twists" life will hand me in the future, I can still move forward because I respect myself enough to do the work. I am proud of how far I've come since eating disorders, divorce, depression, and beyond.

You should be proud of the steps you're taking for yourself too. Keep going. Embrace positive and constructive access, even when it's convicting and hard.

Hugs and love to you,
Mel

P.S. Revisit this workbook as often as you need! Set a reminder in your phone for a few months from now. A little pause to reflect reevaluate always does my heart some good.

TODAY'S ADVANCE WORK:

REFLECTION AND APPLICATION

What have you learned about yourself, and how will you continue your advance work from here?

_____

_____

_____

_____

_____

_____

_____

_____

_____

_____

REMINDER

You will make mistakes along the way.

Keep learning and keep going!

ABOUT
MELANIE
LENTZ

Melanie Lentz was born and raised in the High Desert of Southern California. She attended California Baptist University, receiving her bachelor's and master's degrees in kinesiology. In 2007, she was hired by the Secret Service and became a special agent. Her initial assignment was the Los Angeles Field Office. She worked fraud, electronic crimes, protective intelligence, and protection operations. In between her daily investigative assignments, she completed countless protection assignments, both domestic and abroad, for the nation's leaders, foreign heads of state visiting the U.S., as well as presidential candidates during election years.

In 2015, she was reassigned to Former First Lady Nancy Reagan's protection detail. A few months after Mrs. Reagan passed away in 2016,

Melanie made the difficult decision to leave the Secret Service after her personal life was in shatters.

Today, she focuses on protecting herself and becoming the person she's proud to be. She's the author of *Agent Innocent: How the Secret Service Changed My Life*. She's also a regular blogger for Psychology Today and speaks about how the Secret Service taught her to protect herself. In keeping with her college education background, she has a small personal training business and is a virtual swimming coach for Zygo.

When she's not working, she tries to be outside as much as possible (swimming or paddleboarding preferred). She currently resides in the Midwest with her three senior dogs and enjoys living closer to her family (who relocated from Southern California to the Midwest many years ago). She dreams of being a novelist someday.

CONTACT MELANIE

Website: www.melanielentz.com

Media or Speaking Inquiries: media@melanielentz.com

Instagram: @melanielentzauthor

Facebook: www.facebook.com/melanielentzofficial

Psychology Today Blog: www.psychologytoday.com/us/blog/finding-security

Memoir: *Agent Innocent: How the Secret Service Changed My Life*

Made in the USA
Middletown, DE
02 May 2021